CURSIVE PRACTICE

Peacock

Study each letter to understand the order of strokes.

$\mathcal{A}$ $\mathcal{B}$ $\mathcal{C}$ $\mathcal{D}$ $\mathcal{E}$ $\mathcal{F}$

$\mathcal{G}$ $\mathcal{H}$ $\mathcal{I}$ $\mathcal{J}$ $\mathcal{K}$ $\mathcal{L}$

$\mathcal{M}$ $\mathcal{N}$ $\mathcal{O}$ $\mathcal{P}$ $\mathcal{Q}$ **or** $\mathcal{Q}$ $\mathcal{R}$

$\mathcal{S}$ $\mathcal{T}$ $\mathcal{U}$ $\mathcal{V}$ $\mathcal{W}$ $\mathcal{X}$

$\mathcal{Y}$ $\mathcal{Z}$ a b c d

e f g h i j

k l m n o p

q r s t u v

w x y z

apple   boat   car

A *A* *a*

a *a* *a*

B *B* *B*

b *b* *b*

C *C* *C*

c *c* *c*

dog

elephant

frog

$\mathcal{D}$ $\mathcal{D}$ $\mathcal{D}$

d d d

$\mathcal{E}$ $\mathcal{E}$ $\mathcal{E}$

e e e

$\mathcal{F}$ $\mathcal{F}$ $\mathcal{F}$

f f f

goat

hen

ice cream

G G G

g g g

H H H

h h h

I I I

i i i

jacket   *kangaroo*   *lion*

mouse   nuts   octopus

parrot   quail   rabbit

snail   tractor   umbrella

veggies   *whale*   *fox*

$\mathcal{V}$ $\mathcal{V}$ $\mathcal{V}$

v v v

$\mathcal{W}$ $\mathcal{W}$ $\mathcal{W}$

w w w

$\mathcal{X}$ $\mathcal{X}$ $\mathcal{X}$

x x x

yarn

zebra

$\mathcal{Y}$ $\mathcal{Y}$ $\mathcal{Y}$

y y y

$\mathcal{Z}$ $\mathcal{Z}$ $\mathcal{Z}$

$\mathcal{Z}$ $\mathcal{Z}$ $\mathcal{Z}$

My name is

Alligator

apple

Alligator likes apples.

Bear

bike

Bear rides a bike.

Cat

cream

Cat drinks cream.

Duck

doughnut

Duck eats a doughnut.

Eagle

egg

Eagle has an egg.

Fox

flower

Fox smells a flower.

Giraffe

gloves

Giraffe wears gloves.

Hedgehog

hat

Hedgehog wears a hat.

Iguana

ice cream

Iguana eats ice cream.

jaguar

jumps

jaguar jumps for joy.

Koala

keyboard

Koala plays keyboard.

Lion

lemonade

Lion pours lemonade.

Mouse

motorcycle

Mouse rides a motorcycle.

Narwhal

napkin

Narwhal uses a napkin.

Otter

officer

Otter is an officer.

Peacock

pants

Peacock wears pants.

Quail

quilt

Quail makes a quilt.

Raccoon

races

Raccoon runs a race.

Sloth

sleeps

Sloth likes to sleep.

Turtle

tea

Turtle drinks tea.

Unicorn

unique

Unicorn is unique.

Vulture

van

Vulture drives a van.

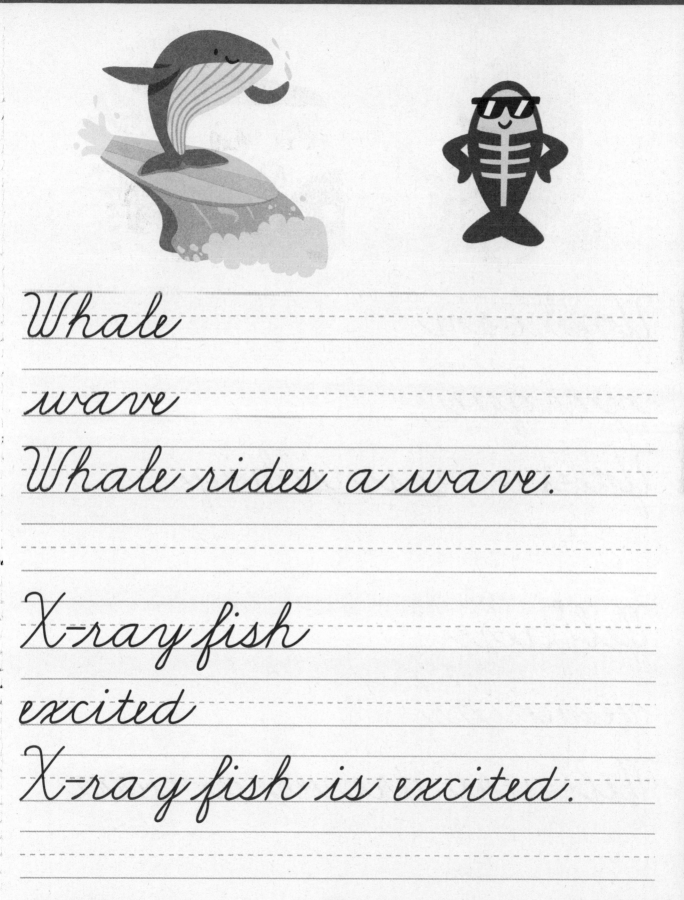

Whale

wave

Whale rides a wave.

X-ray fish

excited

X-ray fish is excited.

Yak

yellow

Yak wears yellow.

Zebra

zinnias

Zebra waters zinnias.

sister, brother, mother,
baby, boy, girl,
friend, family

cake, birthday, card,
gift, bow, wish, box,
candles, balloons

bus, car, plane, ticket,

suitcase, hotel, visit,

train, boat

Monday, Tuesday, Wednesday, Thursday, Friday, Saturday, Sunday

January, February, March, April, May, June, July, August, September, October, November, December

What month is your birthday?

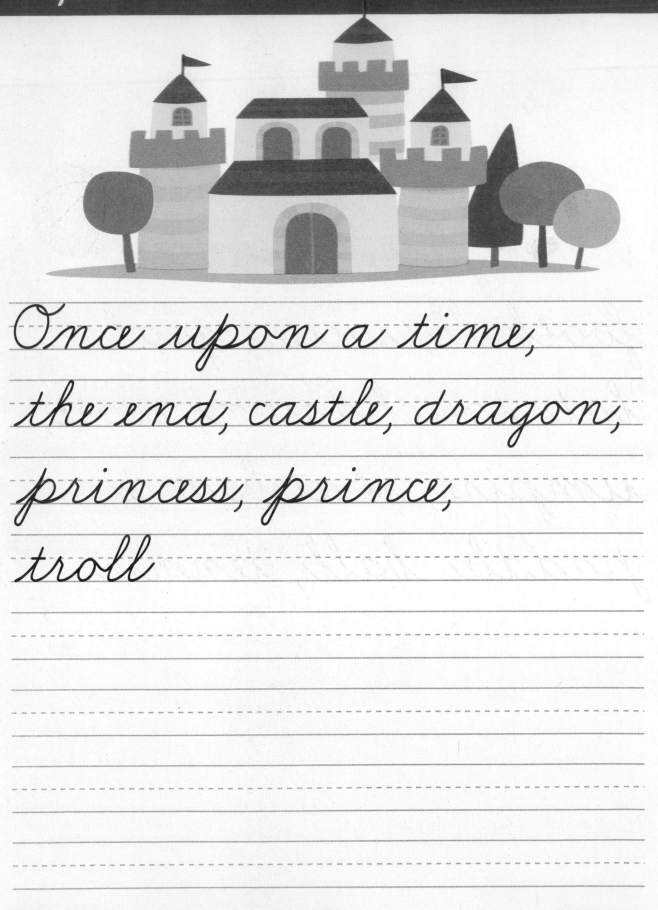

Once upon a time,
the end, castle, dragon,
princess, prince,
troll

football, soccer, goal,

bat, touchdown, score,

umpire, skateboard,

paddle, ball, tennis

apple, banana, salad,

pudding, cookie, cheese,

doughnut, hot dog,

sandwich, dessert, milk